Raising Positive Kids in a Negative World

a handbook for parents & teachers

Virginia Jennison Smith, Ed.D

THE ROADRUNNER PRESS

The RoadRunner Press
Oklahoma City, Oklahoma
www.TheRoadRunnerPress.com

Bulk copies or group sales of this book are available by
contacting orders@theroadrunnerpress.com or calling (405) 524-6205.

Printed in the USA
978-1-937054-46-5 (Trade Paperback)
978-1-937054-47-2 (eBook)

Library of Congress Control Number: 2016933560

Publisher's Cataloging-In-Publication Data
(Prepared by The Donohue Group, Inc.)

Names: Smith, Virginia Jennison.
Title: Raising positive kids in a negative world : a handbook for parents
    & teachers / Virginia Jennison Smith, Ed.D.
Description: Oklahoma City, Oklahoma : RoadRunner Press, [2016] | Includes
    bibliographical references.
Identifiers: LCCN 2016933560 | ISBN 978-1-937054-46-5 (trade paperback) |
    ISBN 978-1-937054-47-2 (ebook)
Subjects: LCSH: Children--Conduct of life--Handbooks, manuals, etc. |
    Child rearing--Handbooks, manuals, etc. | Parenting--Handbooks, manuals, etc. |
Child psychology--Handbooks, manuals, etc.
Classification: LCC BJ1631 .S65 2016 (print) | LCC BJ1631 (ebook) | DDC
    170.83--dc23

10 9 8 7 6 5 4 3 2 1

To Pat

Table of Contents

Introduction

As a parent, guardian, or someone who cares for children, it may seem at times as though the world is fast becoming a scarier and more dangerous place in which to live. Turn on the evening news, read a daily newspaper, or browse the Internet, and you are often inundated with negative stories—examples of deprivation and violence by our fellow man that threaten to shake us to our very core.

How do we raise our children in such a time as this, one in which people seem to learn to hate each other at such an early age, committing violence against their neighbors, classmates, family members, and random strangers? How do we raise children to be positive, loving, compassionate, happy, and trustworthy individuals in such a negative world?

First, we must remind ourselves this is nothing new. Society has always struggled in one form or another with oppression, violence, and a lack of civility. The only difference now is these influences can more easily slip into our daily lives and impact our schools and homes. Indeed, thanks to the Internet and social media, they can seem almost ubiquitous.

We cannot control what the world does around us, but we can focus on our own behavior and how we respond to daily life. By teaching our children good character and modeling what it means to be a kind, compassionate, and civilized person, we can point them in a positive direction and override the negative messages they receive from the outside world.

In the following pages, you will learn how to shape your child's character and why this is one of your most important jobs as a parent. I use the word *shape* on purpose. Some believe character is something you are born with and cannot change, but research has proven that individuals are in fact molded and shaped by external influences.

For most of your child's life, you will have the greatest influence on them, and you will be in the best position to help them become kind, caring, confident, and compassionate individuals. You can build within them the character strength they need in order to withstand the negative forces in life when you can't be with them—and to be a light in the darkness for others.

— Virginia Jennison Smith

How to Use This Book

Each chapter in this book presents a specific concept. First, we will explore what that concept means and how it applies to you as a parent, guardian, caregiver, or mentor. We also share ways to teach that concept to your children—from preschoolers to teenagers. At the end of each teaching section you will also find questions for personal reflection. You may use these as a solitary exercise or to prompt discussion with a spouse, friend, or small group.

Each chapter includes two scenarios: one for younger children and one for teens. I find that one of the best ways to teach something is to tell a story followed by discussion about the issues raised by the tale. Sometimes this makes a concept more vivid and relatable for children, and it can give those who would otherwise not contribute a way to share their story. Read one or both of the scenarios, and then use the Discussion Starters to draw out specific points and make real-life applications.

Whether you study this book in a small group, read it on your own, or work through it with your spouse or child, I hope by its end that you will be inspired and equipped to set about raising a new generation of positive kids.

1. Concepts and examples in this book can apply to parents, grandparents, aunts, uncles, caregivers, mentors, and others. However, for the sake of space and simplicity, we will use a single word such as "parent" or "families" in the rest of this book. Please substitute the right term for your situation.

2. Character qualities and definitions used in this book are drawn from the Elementary Character curriculum published by Character First Education.

Positive

· · · · · · · · ·

good or useful : thinking
that a good result will
happen : hopeful or
optimistic

Chapter 1
Positive Kids

Let's face it—we live in a negative world, and if we're not careful, negative influences can profoundly affect us and our families. It takes constant and intentional effort to be positive in a negative environment, and pushing against the negative grain creates stress in our lives.

This particular type of stress, caused when your inward values conflict with outside influences, can have a negative impact of its own. Instead of strengthening our inner moral compass, we often try to resolve such tension by shifting our values so we fit into the culture. This might ease the stress for a short time, but new situations and more negative influences will soon press us to modify our values again. Like a swimmer caught in a riptide, we look up one day and realize how far we have drifted away from our values and how much ground we have lost to negative influences.

This "values drift" does not need to happen. It is not an inevitable consequence of living in a negative world. If we are proactive and intentional in our approach to life, we can provide a safe haven for our children where they do not have to constantly push against the negative grain. We can provide a place where they feel encouraged in their good choices and behavior, and parenting can take on a positive and supportive role instead of being constantly negative.

Your effort to model and encourage good character will help create a positive culture in your home—a culture where children feel good about doing the right thing. This culture will do a lot of the heavy lifting for you, becoming a positive influence that prevails over the negative messages your children receive. Creating a warm, healthy, encouraging, and uplifting environment will help your children develop a positive outlook on life, a key step toward becoming a successful and well-adjusted adult.

In 1993, a researcher named Richard Wiseman placed an advertisement in a newspaper. He asked people who believed they were "lucky" or "unlucky" to contact him. He gave each of them a newspaper and asked them to count the pictures inside. An interesting thing happened. People who believed themselves to be unlucky completed the task in about two minutes, while the lucky individuals finished in just seconds. What was the difference? On the second page of the newspaper an advertisement instructed participants to stop reading because there were forty-three pictures. The lucky people spotted the information and processed it, while the unlucky folks missed it.

Inside the newspaper a few more pages, a second advertisement informed readers that if they found this ad, they would win a cash prize. The results were the same—spotted by the lucky ones and missed by the unlucky.

What is the lesson of Wiseman's research? Simply, that a strong correlation exists between having a positive perspective or attitude and achieving success. As Wiseman goes on to point out in his research, success has less to do with luck or good fortune and more to do with a person's determination to overcome challenges and make progress, even when progress is difficult.

According to Wiseman, people often "create their own luck" by seizing opportunities and working through problems. These people exhibit several characteristics:

1. They create and notice opportunities.
Do you know someone who seems to always notice when things go on sale or when a new business opportunity presents itself? These individuals are very alert to the world around them. They open their eyes to new opportunities and aren't afraid to take reasonable risks.

2. They heed intuition when making decisions.
Instead of hesitating too long or remaining on the sidelines, lucky people listen when their hearts and their heads urge them to action. This does not mean they are hasty or reckless. Quite the opposite—they consider the options, choose a course of action, and make the best of their decision.

3. They create positive self-fulfilling prophecies.
Lucky people envision a positive future or outcome. Like the *Little Engine That Could*, they tell themselves they are capable of doing their best and reaching their goals. Having a positive vision for the future leads them to act in ways that turn that vision into reality.

4. They turn bad situations into good ones.
Lucky people look for the good in each situation or setback. They don't let hardship or tragedy keep them down; they are resilient. Having a positive attitude gives them the energy they need to overcome challenges and come out better and stronger in the end.

In the following chapters, we will discuss how you can become a positive influence on the children in your life—whether you're a parent, a teacher, a grandparent, or a coach, and how those same children can be encouraged to adopt a positive attitude in their own lives.

Personal Reflection
1. Think of people who are positive and optimistic. How do they differ from others? What do they do that identifies them as a positive person? What are some things they say?

2. When you first start your day, what are some things that can have a negative impact on how you feel?

3. Positive people notice the small, positive things in life. Do you believe you can train yourself and others to notice the positive? How might this be done?

4. How does negative interaction with others affect your mood? Can you recognize when this happens? When you recognize negativity is bringing you down, what can you do to reverse course?

5. How can a positive attitude help you work through problems and challenges?

6. How can creating a positive picture of your future help you be more positive? How can you help your children create a positive vision for their future?

Child Scenario:
Ashley's Great Day

Ashley woke up in a bad mood. All she could think about was how her brother had gotten to go to the zoo yesterday and she hadn't. The more she thought about it, the grouchier she became. She could hear her family in the kitchen making breakfast. Soon one of them would come tell her it was time to eat before going to school.

Sure enough, in just a few minutes her brother came to her room. "Get up sleepy head, it's time to eat!" he said.

Ashley, still feeling mad about yesterday, slowly made her way downstairs. She found her grandma just putting scrambled eggs on Ashley's plate. Before she could sit down, Grandma greeted Ashley, "Good morning sunshine. How is Grandma's favorite girl doing?" Ashley couldn't help but smile. Her grandma had a gift for making even the worst days seem bearable. "I'm just tired," Ashley replied as she gobbled down her eggs and a piece of buttered toast.

After she finished eating, Ashley went upstairs where her mother had picked out her favorite shirt to wear. It was brightly colored with a sparkly rainbow on the front. "You will look so cute in that shirt," her mother said.

Ashley got dressed, and as her mother brushed her hair, her mom told her: "You are a sweet girl with a beautiful heart." Ashley could feel herself become a little happier as she gave her mother a good-bye hug.

When Ashley boarded the school bus, her friend Susan was waiting for her, having saved Ashley a seat. The two friends began to happily chatter away. When the bus arrived at school, Ashley went into her classroom. It was Monday, which meant it was spelling test day. Ashley felt good about the test. Her brother had spent extra time helping her study after he got home from the zoo, and Ashley knew that she knew the words. Even her brother had expressed confidence that she would do well.

As her teacher, Mr. Fallgatter, slowly read the words off one by one, Ashley quickly wrote down her answers. When Ashley turned in her paper, Mr. Fallgatter observed, "Ashley, I can tell you did very well. You studied and you knew the words. I'm glad to have such a diligent student in my class."

Ashley beamed. Even though she had started her day feeling grumpy and out of sorts, as each hour passed she felt better. She ended the day grateful and happy, and couldn't wait to get home to tell her family about her day—and to give her brother a big hug for having helped her study.

Discussion Starters

1. How did Ashley's day begin? Was she in a good mood or a bad mood? Why? Did her attitude color how she felt at the beginning of the day?

2. What was one of the first things that helped Ashley feel better? Do you think her grandma's words helped Ashley have a better attitude about her day? What have other people told you to make you feel better?

3. How did Ashley's mother help? How do you think giving her mother a hug affected Ashley and her mother? How does showing someone you care about them help them be more positive and happy?

4. When Ashley got the chance to talk with a friend, how did that affect her day? Can talking to friends about what's going on help you feel better?

5. Ashley did well on the spelling test—because she studied but also because she had a positive attitude. How can having a positive attitude help you do better in school?

6. How do you think it helped Ashley's attitude to say thank-you to her brother at the end of the day? How did it make her brother feel? Do you think he is more likely to help her in the future because she was grateful instead of grouchy? Why or why not?

Teen Scenario:
The Interview

Addison and Evie were sitting in the entrance area of the Pizza Palace with about twenty other young people their age. Everyone was there to apply for three openings on the wait staff of the popular restaurant. Pizza Palace was always busy and seemed like a fun place to work, and both Addison and Evie desperately wanted the job.

As they waited their turns, Addison and Evie filled out employment applications. Addison thought to herself, These forms are ridiculous. How in the world am I supposed to remember every place I have ever worked and the dates I worked there. The more questions she read and tried to answer, the more discouraged and upset Addison became. I know I don't have as much experience as half the people in this room, she thought. There is no way they are going to hire me. In fact, I'm not even sure I want to be hired. I mean, look at these people here and how they are making us wait.

Addison finished the application with a big sigh. This is going to be terrible, she thought as she glared at the people sitting across from her.

Evie was also struggling a bit with some of the questions. She laughed as she recalled some of the other fun places she had worked, like when she worked at the Burger Lot with Jason and they competed to see who could get the most customers to smile. She paused a moment and looked around the room. There looked to be a lot of qualified people who want this job. But she reminded herself that it had been the same when she applied at the Burger Lot. I'm just going to have to smile and be myself, she thought. I'll try my best and see what happens.

Evie smiled at Jonathan who was sitting across the room from her. She whispered, "Good luck!" when his name was called for an interview. Evie looked at the application form in her hand. You've got this, she told herself. Just go in there and show them what you can do. The man calling names looked around, and Evie smiled back at him. "Addison O'Neal, you're next followed by Evie Mendez," he announced.

Addison frowned, grabbed her application form, and slowly walked into her interview. When she came back to the waiting area ten minutes later, Evie smiled and gave Addison a big hug. "Maybe we will both get positions," Evie said as she went cheerfully into her interview.

Discussion Starters

1. How can having a positive outlook make you feel? How can your positive attitude affect those around you?

2. How can being negative impact other people's impression of you?

3. Do people tend to gravitate toward positive or negative people?

4. Who do you think has a better chance of getting a job—Addison or Evie? Why?

5. What was the difference between Addison and Evie's outlook on the situation? How different were their approaches to the job interview process?

6. Can being positive increase your chance of being successful in an endeavor? Why or why not?

7. Would you agree that negativity can influence someone? How are people affected when they hear negative things all the time? In contrast, what can people accomplish if they think others believe in them? Why do you think this is the case?

Hello Uncle Sam...

Character

· · · · · · · · ·

the inward values that

determine someone's

outward actions

Chapter 2
Shaping Character

In July 1944, the young author Anne Frank wrote in her famous wartime diary:

> *"I understand more and more how true Daddy's words were when he said: 'All children must look after their own upbringing.' Parents can only give good advice or put them on the right paths, but the final forming of a person's character lies in their own hands."*

Parents shape the character of their children by leading, teaching, encouraging, and pointing children down the right path. Ideally, their children will grow up to understand and embrace the right path for themselves, building on the foundation that their parents provided.

Wise parents know little eyes are always watching, and as the old saying goes, "Your walk talks and your talk talks. But your walk talks louder than your talk talks." The first and foremost way a parent shapes a child's character is by modeling positive attitudes and behaviors on a consistent basis. This means being patient, respectful, courteous, and kind—even when it is difficult. It means being honest, diligent, loyal, and true—even when it is not easy. In fact, especially then. However, modeling character does not mean you have to be perfect. Some of life's greatest lessons are taught through failure. Don't be afraid to admit your mistakes and tell your children what you learned from them. Encourage them to learn from your mistakes so they can avoid unnecessary trouble and heartache themselves. Show them how to handle failure, make things right, and move on.

Life is full of opportunities to point out to children the benefits of good character and the consequences of bad character in daily life. Look for "teachable moments" in your local news, sporting events, personal relationships, school activities, and life at work. Take time to explain why you behaved in certain ways or made certain decisions. Share what's going on inside your heart and mind so that your children learn how to apply personal values when they are faced with similar choices in their own lives.

Help your children develop a rich vocabulary of character words so they can discuss and deal with ethical issues. You might focus on one character quality at a time. Define what it is, give examples of how it applies to daily life, and then look for ways to reinforce it during the week or month. Then move on to another character quality.

When you talk about qualities such as honesty, responsibility, and self-control, be sure to include yourself in the conversation. Instead of saying, "You need to be honest," say something like, "We all need to be honest" or "Honesty is important for everyone, including me." Make sure to provide practical ways to live out a character quality. Give your children real-life examples, and ask them for their own ideas. Encourage them to think of how a character quality might help them grow and develop as a person.

When you notice a child demonstrating good character through attitude and behavior—celebrate it. Use specific language, including the character vocabulary, to point out what you appreciate. You might say, "I noticed you put your toys away without being asked. I appreciate your initiative. You're a big help around here." Or maybe something like, "Great job on your test. I noticed how diligent and attentive you were while studying. Looks like it made a difference."

This kind of positive reinforcement goes deeper than just saying something vague, generic, or cliché, like "Good job!" or "Awesome!" If you want a child to value your compliments, they need to be specific and include actions your child has taken and the benefits that came from the choices made. This makes your encouragement genuine, believable, and inspiring.

When children do something wrong, be sure you address the underlying character issue, not just the surface actions. This is because outward actions flow from our inward values. A child forgetting an assignment might reveal a lack of responsibility, diligence, or orderliness. Fighting over a toy might reveal a problem with anger or greed. Cheating on a test might reveal the need to develop honesty and moral courage. Trying to fix the outward action without resolving the heart issue is like putting a bucket under a leaky roof instead of fixing the roof. In time, the problem will only return or manifest itself in a different way.

Having a rich character vocabulary can help you deal with heart issues by providing the questions to ask your child in such moments:

Was that being responsible?

Were you being diligent?

Was that showing respect to your brother?

How can you show self-control in this situation?

Was that an honest thing to do?

It can be tempting to modify or control a child's behavior by making up more rules. Unfortunately, more rules often lead to more creative rule-breakers, and it is impossible to generate enough rules to cover every possible scenario in life. Besides, who will be there to enforce your rules every minute of the day? And what happens when the child grows up and gets to make his or her own rules?

This is why children need to learn principles of character so they can make good choices regardless of whether a rule has been written or someone is there to enforce it. When you talk about rules, try to explain the principles involved so that children understand why the rules exist. This will make the rule seem less arbitrary, and children will understand the purpose and spirit of the rule, not just the letter of it.

Personal Reflection

1. What are some of the rules in your household? What are some of the ways you might be able to honor those rules but state them in a positive, character-based manner? For example "Don't hit your brother" might become "Show respect for your

brother." How does a restatement in a positive, principle-based manner actually rule out other aggressive behaviors so that every situation doesn't have to be addressed by an individual rule?

2. What are some of the behaviors you would like to see your children demonstrate? What are some ways you can state these positively using character-specific language?

3. Why is it necessary to deal with heart issues, not just surface actions? Think about a recent behavior you had to correct. What were some of the heart issues behind that behavior?

Child Scenario:
Daniel's Rotten Day

Daniel was so frustrated. He had been waiting a long time for Natalie to stop using the little model cars and track so he could have a turn with them. Finally he had enough. He marched over to Natalie and grabbed the red car she was holding out of her hand and pushed her away. Natalie immediately began to cry.

Mrs. Hale, the teacher, came right over to see why Natalie was crying. "Daniel took the car," Natalie explained, "and he pushed me like this." Natalie raised both of her arms and dramatically pushed at the teacher.

"Daniel," said Mrs. Hale, "you're in time out."

As she took Daniel to the time out chair, she asked him why he had taken the car and pushed Natalie. "She wouldn't stop playing," said Daniel, "and I wanted a turn."

"Do you know why you're in trouble?" asked Mrs. Hale. Daniel shook his head no. "It's because you took the car from Natalie and you pushed her."

"But I didn't hit Natalie!" said Daniel. "The rule says not to hit anyone. I only pushed her a little."

"I'm sorry you didn't understand, Daniel. Maybe we should say the rule this way: 'Respect everyone and be kind.' That way you would know that you should treat everyone kindly. When you took the car away and pushed Natalie, that wasn't kind, was it?" asked Mrs. Hale, gently.

"No," said Daniel, "I'm sorry I did that to Natalie. Next time I will be kind and I promise to respect her. I will ask her if it is okay if I play with the toys instead of trying to take things away."

"Thank you," said Mrs. Hale, "We all learned something today. You learned to be kind and show respect, and I learned how to help you understand better how to behave."

Discussion Starters

1. Tell about a time when you felt like Daniel. What did you do?

2. Do you think it was fair that Daniel was punished? Why or why not?

3. If Daniel didn't technically break the rules, why do you think he got in trouble?

4. What are some kind or respectful ways Daniel could let Mrs. Hale and Natalie know he would like to play?

Teen Scenario:
Pep Rally!

Ashton took the poster boards out of her trunk and carried them into the gym. Dani, Courtney, and Desi were there waiting for her with paints and markers in hand.

"Let's get started," said Dani. "We only have an hour before they start setting up for the pep rally, and we have to be out of the way before then."

Each girl took two poster boards and a few markers and started to work. They were just getting started, when Vice Principal Jones walked in and saw what they were doing. He got a stern look on his face.

"Remember, ladies," Mr. Jones admonished, "no profanity and no curse words on those signs. You know what happened the last time."

The girls turned to each other, and Courtney muttered, "Yeah, we remember. Jess got suspended because she held up a bad word for the entire senior class to see."

Dani and Desi giggled as they recalled Mr. Jones's red face as he marched over to Jess in front of the whole assembly and took the sign, earning jeers from the seniors.

After Mr. Jones left them to their work, it wasn't long before Courtney got a mischievous look on her face. She began to draw on her poster with a large red marker. After she finished she held up the poster to show the other girls.

On Courtney's poster were a couple of slogans about the opposing team that included some words that were very similar to bad language, but not exactly. She had substituted a couple of almost identical words where the curse words were supposed to go, and then underlined them. She was pleased that she had technically followed the rule, but still had written what she wanted.

25

Discussion Starters

1. Did Courtney technically follow the vice principal's rule? How did she get around the rule? Do you think this is a good idea?

2. How do you think Mr. Jones is going to react if Courtney holds her sign up during the pep rally?

3. What are some possible outcomes if Courtney holds up the sign?

4. What is a different way the school could state the rule that would encourage Courtney to not create a sign like she did?

5. How is a positively stated guideline more likely to avoid a situation like this than a Do Not Rule?

Consistency

· · · · · · · · · ·

harmony of conduct
or practice

Chapter 3
Consistency

In the world of education, teachers strive every day to help their students develop mastery of material. This means training students to understand the subject matter well enough to pass an exam or be able to explain the concept to someone else. After consistently demonstrating mastery of a subject, students move to the next level of learning.

Mastery involves consistency, the ability to produce the same results over an extended period of time. Consistency is based on a pattern of success—a habit of thought and behavior. When children consistently demonstrate good character, we learn to trust them more and more. This leads to new opportunities, responsibilities, and the privileges that come with maturity. As trust grows, we spend less effort repairing broken relationships and more energy working together to new levels of success.

Dr. Nathan Mellor, chief executive officer of Strata Leadership, developed the C3 Model:

Character (C1) + Competence (C2) = Consistency (C3)

If you want to change the consistent results or outcomes, you have to change the factors that go into the equation. Someone's consistency is actually the sum of two components: character and competence.

Character describes the set of inner values a person uses to make decisions, and this determines a person's attitudes and behaviors. When you combine the values of every family member, you get a "family character" that includes the cultural norms and values that generally guide decisions and behavior.

Competence is the second part of the "consistency equation." Competence is a person's ability to do something well as measured against a common standard. Having good character is not enough to succeed. For example, you probably want a competent surgeon—not just a *nice* person—operating on you. Competence means you have the technical knowledge and skills needed to be proficient in a task.

With a high level of character and a high level of competence, children will consistently produce a higher level of success. If a child's behavior or performance is not satisfactory, understanding this equation can help you identify if the problem is a character issue or a competence issue so you can correctly address the problem.

Look at the following list of behavioral challenges. Which ones do you think are character issues? Which ones reveal a lack of competence? And which challenges reveal a deficiency of both character and competence?

Lying
Miscommunication
Hasty decisions
Exaggerating

Gossiping
Shifting blame
Not paying attention
Not completing homework or tasks
Being disrespectful
Inappropriate language
Apathy
Wasting time or other resources
Lateness
Messy or disorganized
Moodiness
Not considering consequences

Some challenges are clearly character, others competence, and many are a combination of the two. If children have a perpetually messy room, this might reveal a character issue such as laziness or apathy. However, they also just might not know how to organize themselves or their environment, which is a competence issue. Perhaps you need to teach this skill and coach them through the process until it becomes a habit. Understanding the relationship between character, competence, and consistency will help you address challenges more effectively and equip your children with the head knowledge and heart attitudes needed for success.

Personal Reflection

1. What are some of your core values? How do you communicate these to family members?

2. Is it possible for a group of people (a family, a group of friends, or colleagues) to agree on a set of

values? Why or why not?

3. How do your values affect your decisions? What impact do values have on your behavior?

4. How do your values differ from other family members, friends, or society? How do these differences affect you or your family?

5. Can values change over time? What might cause you to change your values?

Child Scenario:
Nicki Doesn't Give Up

Nicki was so frustrated. Mrs. Robson had just finished explaining how to multiply by nine when she passed out the practice sheet. Nicki stared hopelessly at the three rows and three columns of equations that required multiplication by nine. Math just isn't my thing, Nicki told herself. Mrs. Robson drones on and on about this and that, and then she expects us to understand right away.

Nicki glanced over at Clara who was quickly going equation by equation and writing an answer. She wondered how Clara did it. She thought about how she tried to listen to Mrs. Robson but the room was so hot. Nicki glanced down at her empty paper, except this time she remembered to write her name at the top. By now, Clara was on the next to last problem. I don't have time to think about this right now, thought Nicki. What if I copy Clara's answers just this once and then use them to go back and learn this stuff on my own. Nicki considered the idea.

Discussion Starters

1. Do you think it is okay for Nicki to copy Clara's answers since she intends to go back and learn the material later?

2. How likely do you think it is that Nicki will actually go back and learn the material if she copies Clara's answers?

3. Is it okay for Nicki to copy Clara's answers if she asks Clara first and Clara says it is okay?

4. What can Nicki do if she decides to not copy Clara's answers? What are her other options?

5. How do you think Mrs. Robson will respond if she catches Nicki copying Clara's answers?

6. How do you think Mrs. Robson will respond if Nicki raises her hand, admits she is struggling, and asks for help?

7. What can Nicki say if and when she asks Mrs. Robson for help?

Teen Scenario:
Davon's Dilemma

Davon and his mom had recently moved from their home in Chicago to Evansville, a town in rural Iowa. Davon had always been athletic and had played on the school basketball team, starting as a forward. In fact, Davon had been team captain prior to his dad's death and his mother's decision to move to Evansville to be closer to family. Now Davon was in a new town that was drastically different from his fast-paced life in Chicago. He felt like a fish out of water.

Not only did the little town have a slower pace, but basketball was not nearly as popular as football in this rural town. Davon decided that if he was going to make friends quickly, he needed to practice and try out for the football team.

Day one and two went well. Davon went out to the football field with his ball and practiced running patterns. He was a quick study and became quite good at pivoting and turning on the turf. However, on day three when Davon arrived at the field to practice running plays, he saw four members of the varsity squad playing a game of flag football. They were so much better than he was. After watching for about half an hour, Davon turned around and headed home.

Discussion Starters

1. How do you think Davon is feeling after watching the varsity players on the field?

2. How do you think Davon's feelings about the four varsity players impacted his decision to stay at practice or go home?

3. Is Davon experiencing a problem of character, competence, or both? Why do you think this?

4. What are some choices Davon faces? Do you think he will eventually decide to practice and get better, or will he decide to quit? Why do you think this?

5. What would you do if you were in Davon's shoes?

6. What other things about Davon's circumstances could be influencing his behavior and choices? Why might these things have an effect?

7. What can Davon's mother do to help him?

8. Do you think Davon should keep trying to play football, or is there another option that is better for him? Why do you think this?

Responsibility

· · · · · · · · · ·

taking   ownership
of   my   thoughts,
words, and actions

Chapter 4
Responsibility

Part of human nature is the tendency to blame others when things go wrong instead of taking ownership of one's actions. It is easier to blame the economy than to admit I made a poor financial decision. It is easier to say, "He really provoked me," than to admit, "I was wrong when I lost my temper." Or the classic: "How was I supposed to know the coffee was hot?" instead of, "I wasn't careful and spilled hot coffee on myself."

The trouble with shifting blame instead of taking responsibility is you behave as if you have no control over your situation. As a result, you do not learn from mistakes, which means you limit yourself from growing and improving. You simply continue blaming others for your bad decisions.

For several years I worked at a university where I helped students from under-prepared backgrounds succeed at college. Unfortunately, many of the students viewed themselves as victims of circumstance instead of taking responsibility for their situations. So when students failed an exam, I would often hear them explain the room was too hot, the syllabus was unclear, the book was too difficult to understand, or the professor didn't adequately prepare them for the test. While one or more of these factors might have been true, the real problem usually boiled down to choices the students had made—staying up too late the night before, not completing homework, not studying for the test, or skipping class. Once students owned up to their contribution to the problem, they could correct the situation and succeed at the next exam.

Responsibility means taking ownership of your thoughts, words, and actions. It is a key characteristic of successful people and the first character quality we will explore in this book.

It can be frustrating when a boss sets a goal or gives you a task that is unachievable. Even worse, is when that goal or expectation was not communicated and you are blamed for not achieving something you didn't know you were supposed to do in the first place. One way to help children practice responsibility is to carefully manage expectations. Give clear instructions so your children know what they are supposed to do and ask for their verbal agreement: "I need you to take responsibility for your room and clean it up before dinner. Can you do that?" or "We need to leave the house tomorrow morning by 7:00 a.m. Can I count on you to be ready?"

Sometimes you might need to lower your expectations because of time or circumstance. It might be reasonable to expect a spotless room before company arrives if children have an hour or two to work on their rooms. But if they only have ten minutes, you might say something like, "Wow, your room is a mess and company arrives for lunch in ten minutes. Let's work together to straighten things up the best we can, and after our company leaves I want you to clean your room more thoroughly. That means put everything where it belongs, dust the furniture, empty the trash, and vacuum. Do you think you can finish cleaning your room before we eat supper at 6:00 p.m.?"

Encourage children to clarify instructions if they don't understand something. This should be done in a respectful, cooperative manner—not as a way to manipulate, delay, or weasel out of an assignment.

If necessary, help them break a job into smaller tasks or milestones. For example, put things away from 2:00 p.m. to 3:30 p.m., finish dusting by 4:00 p.m., finish vacuuming by 4:30 p.m., and empty the trash by 5:00 p.m. You might need to define terms such as "put things away" so they know that doesn't mean stuffing everything under the bed.

A responsible person cares about doing things right the first time. As the famous college basketball coach John Wooden would say, "If you don't have time to do it right, when will you have time to do it over?"

When you make a mistake, responsibility means owning up to the mistake and doing what you can to make things right. It is difficult to admit you have done something wrong, but this is a natural part of learning, growing, and relating to one another. Sometimes the wording is difficult, too. As journalist Sydney J. Harris observed in his 1964 book, *On the Contrary*: "We have not passed that subtle line between childhood and adulthood until we move from the passive voice to the active voice—that is, until we have stopped saying, 'It got lost,' and say, 'I lost it.'"

When children are proactive about admitting their mistakes, thank them for being honest and taking responsibility. Give them a soft place to land so they learn over time it is better to admit mistakes and make things right than to cover up what they have done. Even though it is stretching or uncomfortable at times, taking responsibility is necessary to experience success. By teaching children to be responsible, we empower them to take control of their lives through the choices they make.

Personal Reflection

1. Why is it important to set clear expectations for your children and to make sure they understand what is expected?

2. What are some expectations you have of your children? Do they know what these expectations are? How do they know? How have you communicated these expectations?

3. What are some excuses you hear regularly at your house? How can you help your children to recognize when they are making excuses? How can you help them take ownership of the situation instead of making excuses?

4. When you make excuses or shift blame, how does this steal power from yourself?

5. What motivates you or inspires you to do your best? What can you do to help motivate your children?

6. What keeps you going when you are tired or frustrated? How can you teach your children to fulfill what they need to do even when they are discouraged?

Child Scenario:
Too Many Tasks

It was Saturday, Garette's favorite day of the week. On top of it being Saturday, it was sunny, warm, and Garette's Aunt Kenzie was in town. That meant one fabulous thing—time to go to the zoo. Garette loved the zoo. He loved walking around, seeing the cool animals, hanging out with Aunt Kenzie, and getting ice cream.

Garette's mom stuck her head in the bedroom. "Time to get up, Garette!" she called. "Aunt Kenzie will be here by lunchtime and you have to finish cleaning your room before you can go to the zoo."

Oh no, thought Garette as he looked frantically around his room at the mess. His action figures were on the floor where he had left them after playing last night, his dirty clothes were not in the hamper, and his model building bricks were . . . everywhere. It's not like this was a surprise. Mother had asked him to clean his room two days ago. Garette had agreed to do it then, but he'd forgotten. And he promised it would be clean before Aunt Kenzie came to take him to the zoo. Now he looked around in a panic. How was he going to finish in time?

Discussion Starters

1. What job did Garette agree to do? When did he make that agreement?

2. What is the consequence of Garette not cleaning his room when he was asked two days ago?

3. What might happen if Garette doesn't finish?

4. Whose fault would it be if Garette doesn't get to go to the zoo? Mother's fault for asking him to clean his room? Aunt Kenzie's fault for coming at noon? Or Garette's fault for not cleaning his room when he first agreed to do it?

5. What can Garette do now to fix the situation?

Teen Scenario:
A Net Bomb

It was the first practice of the season. Clara had joined a community volleyball league with her best friend Sara and they were on a team called the Net Bombers named after the local Air Force base. The coach, who also happened to be Sara's dad, divided the group of twelve into two teams of six for a scrimmage so he could see everyone's skill and what they brought to the team.

Sara and Clara were on the Red team and positioned next to each other on the volleyball court, right by the net. They giggled nervously as neither of them had ever played organized volleyball before, just quick games with friends.

The coach blew the whistle, and the other team served the ball. It sailed over the net toward Sara and Clara, but at no one in particular. Both Clara and Sara stared at the ball and then looked at each other. The ball hit the ground in between them.

Sara's dad yelled, "One point for Team Blue!"

The rest of Team Red grumbled as Sara and Clara blushed from embarrassment. Either one of the girls could have returned the ball, but neither of them had stepped up and called "mine!"

Clara went straight home after volleyball practice. Her grandmother was sick, so Clara's mom was away helping clean grandmother's house. This meant it was Clara's job to fix supper for the family. Clara planned on making enchiladas; they would be easy, and her dad and brother both liked them.

Clara got out the casserole dish and went to the pantry to get the enchilada sauce, refried beans, and . . . *tortillas*. Yikes! she had forgotten to pick up tortillas on the way home from practice. Clara yelled upstairs to her brother who was working on his math homework.

"Chad, can you please go to the store and get some tortillas for me?"

"Sure thing," said Chad as he closed his math book and headed downstairs. "I'll be back in ten minutes."

Sure enough, in about ten minutes Clara heard Chad come through the door with a grocery bag in hand. Inside was a big package of flour tortillas.

"Chad, I needed corn tortillas for enchiladas, not flour tortillas," Clara said. "And I need the small size that fits into the casserole dish, not the big ones."

Chad glared at his sister, turned around, and stomped up the stairs. "You're welcome," Clara heard him mutter as he disappeared into his room.

Discussion Starters

1. What does it mean to take ownership of your actions? How could Sara or Clara have taken ownership at volleyball practice? What might have happened if either had called for the ball and tried to return it?

45

2. What expectations did Clara's family have for her when she came home after volleyball practice?

3. What was Clara supposed to do on her way home?

4. What did Clara do when she realized she didn't have what she needed to prepare enchiladas for dinner?

5. What did Clara ask her brother to do? Did Clara's brother understand exactly what she needed? Why or why not?

6. How could Clara have communicated her expectations more clearly?

7. What happened when her brother returned from the store? How did Clara react? Was her reaction fair? Why or why not?

8. How might Clara fix the situation now? How can this situation be avoided next time?

Oh, thank you...

Gratefulness

· · · · · · · · ·

showing appreciation

for what I have

Chapter 5
Gratefulness

Researchers interested in why students persist to graduate from college or the resilience of children in foster care have begun studying the role of gratefulness in personal success. Studies indicate that demonstrating appreciation for what you have and recognizing how others have helped you has a strong correlation when it comes to attaining goals. Grateful people are more likely to reach their goals, bounce back from disappointment or failure, and experience success.

There are two basic parts to gratefulness: recognizing positive things in your life and showing your appreciation for them. Gratefulness means opening your eyes to the benefits you've received and finding ways to express your gratitude to those who have helped you. Grateful people understand they did not get where they are on their own. They recognize how others have helped them.

Grateful people are pleasant to be around. They are cheerful and content. In contrast, ungrateful people are self-centered, presumptuous, and energy-draining. It's a chore to be with people who complain, gripe, and take things for granted.

Do you have a coworker who stays upbeat even when faced with a challenge? Do you have a friend who looks on the bright side even when things go wrong? Do you know people who are grateful for what they have, even though they don't have much? Gratefulness is not based on your circumstances—it is a choice you make to have a positive attitude and express appreciation, even when things don't go exactly as you planned.

Help your children develop this trait by sitting down together and making a Gratefulness List. What do you have as a family that you appreciate? What do your children have that they are grateful for? What are some helpful things others have done for them? What would happen if these things went undone? Are they grateful for basic things in life such as food, clothing, and shelter?

Another way to practice gratefulness is to write thank-you notes. This might seem quaint and old-fashioned, but it is important for your children to express appreciation. Buy some inexpensive thank-you cards or help your children make their own using blank paper. Young children might want to draw pictures or you can write the note based on what they say. Older children can write their own notes with a little coaching.

Start the note with a salutation (Dear Aunt Kenzie) and specifically say what you are grateful for (Thank you for taking me to the zoo). Say how you felt about the gift or action (I had a lot of fun with you and enjoyed learning about the animals). Close the letter with an appropriate ending (Sincerely, Yours Truly, or Love) and sign your name. Teach children how to properly address, stamp, and send the note by mail. If sending an electronic message, you might add a picture to make the note more meaningful. Remember, the sooner you send the note, the more it communicates that you appreciate the person. Teach your children to send thank-yous within two weeks of receiving a gift or making a visit.

Personal Reflection

1. What are some things others have done for you at work? At home? How did you express appreciation for those things?

2. How does being grateful affect your attitude? How does a lack of gratitude affect your attitude?

3. What happens to relationships when someone takes the other for granted?

4. What happens when children think they deserve everything? How might this "entitlement mentality" hinder them in the future?

5. When someone expresses gratefulness to you, what can you say or do in return?

Child Scenario:
David and Darren

It was April, and that meant it was birthday month. David and Darren were twins and shared everything—a room, friends, a family, toys, and of course, a birthday. Mom had been planning their birthday party for quite a while. She had called the local roller skating rink and made a reservation for twenty, including friends and family members. She had sent out invitations and made sure everyone in their class was included. She had bought special plates, napkins, and lots of balloons. When the morning of the party arrived, she went to the local bakery to pick up the cake she had ordered. It was decorated with space ships, planets, moons, and stars because David and Darren loved outer space.

David woke early that morning and raced downstairs. He couldn't wait to get to the skating rink and celebrate with all his friends. He ate breakfast and quickly picked up his dishes and rinsed them in the sink. He went back upstairs, made his bed, took a shower, and got dressed. As the family piled into the car to head to the skating rink, David gave his mom a big hug and said, "Thank you so much!" for all her work putting on the party.

When they arrived at the rink, David greeted each of his friends and thanked them for coming to the party. After cake and ice cream, it was time to open presents. David smiled as he opened each present and said thank you to each person. After a fun time skating, it was time to go home. David thanked everyone again for coming and being a part of the celebration. He even said thank you to the people running the roller skating rink.

Darren, on the other hand, was having a bad day. It seemed like he woke up on the wrong side of the bed, and breakfast only made it worse. He picked at his food for a little while, then got up from the table to get dressed. Darren left his dirty plate on the table, and so his dad had to call him back to the table to get it and take it to the sink. Darren did as he was asked, but grumbled all the way to the sink and then all the way to his room.

Darren was even grumpier when he saw his brother in such a good mood. Darren got cleaned up and dressed for the day, but mom had to remind him twice that it was about time to leave for the party. He dragged himself to the car, leaving his bed unmade. After they arrived at the roller rink, things improved a little but not much. As their friends arrived, they seemed to be more interested in spending time with David than with Darren.

What's up with that, Darren thought.

After cake and ice cream it was time to open presents. Darren opened each present and then set it aside. After the party was over, he climbed back into the family car carrying his favorite gift and made the trip back home. Back in his bedroom, his first thought was, Oh great—now I have to make my bed!

Discussion Starters

1. Who do you think was more fun to be around, David or Darren? Why?

2. Who demonstrated gratefulness, David or Darren? How did he show gratefulness?

3. How do you think David's mom felt when he told her thank you?

4. How do you think it made David feel when he expressed appreciation?

5. How did Darren feel on his birthday?

6. How did Darren's lack of gratefulness affect his mood?

7. How did his lack of gratefulness end up making the others feel? How did you think it made Darren's mother feel?

8. How do you think the rest of David's day would go after the party?

9. How do you think the rest of Darren's day would go after the party?

10. How can Darren change the way he is feeling?

Teen Scenario:
Aria's Recital

Aria was nervous. It was the day of her big piano recital and her whole family was going to be there. Aria had practiced for weeks and knew the piece she planned to perform well, but she still had the jitters. She was more than a little afraid that she would make a noticeable mistake or even worse—forget how to play a single note. Staring in the mirror, Aria reminded herself that everyone who would be in the audience only had her best interest at heart and just wanted to see her succeed.

Aria arrived at the recital hall on time and sat down. Her parents, brother and sister, aunt and uncle, and grandma were all sitting on the second row. Her teacher stood up and called her name—it was time. Aria sat down at the piano and began to play. The music seemed to flow effortlessly from her fingers, and before she knew it she was smiling and bowing to the audience. Her piano teacher gave her a big hug and handed her the microphone, and Aria began to speak.

Discussion Starters

1. Who played a part in Aria's success? Was she the only one?

2. If you were Aria and the teacher handed you the microphone, what would you say?

3. What are some specific things Aria can mention about those who have helped or supported her?

4. How do you think people will feel if Aria takes all the credit for herself? How would that make her appear?

5. Why is it important for Aria to share the credit for her fine performance with others?

6. How does being grateful make Aria feel? How would being ungrateful make her feel?

Honesty

· · · · · · · · ·

being truthful in
what I say and do

Chapter 6
Honesty

Have you ever caught children doing something wrong and immediately they started making up a story about what happened in order to avoid the consequences of their actions? Instead of owning up and telling the truth, they exaggerate facts, obscure information, deny reality, and manipulate the situation. And the crazy thing is—children know how to do this without any training.

Of course, children aren't the only ones who tell lies or skew information in order to get what they want or to get themselves out of trouble. It's a temptation all of us face—whether reporting to someone at work, paying taxes, or interacting with friends and family. Sometimes the truth seems too difficult or painful to face. But ignoring the facts and hiding the truth can cost you something significant: trust.

What everyone needs to understand—including your children—is that trust is the foundation for all relationships. If someone can't trust you, then it makes living with you or doing business with you very difficult. On the other hand, when people enjoy a high level of trust with one another, it makes life easier for everyone involved. Remember, trust is much easier kept than recovered. It takes years to build trust, but only moments to destroy it through a careless act or dishonest deed. That is why "honesty is the best policy" if you want to preserve your relationships, protect your integrity, and be known as a trustworthy person.

Personal Reflection

1. When can it be difficult to tell the truth?

2. Why is trust important in a healthy relationship?

3. What can happen when you aren't entirely honest with someone?

4. Do you think admitting a mistake makes you more or less trustworthy? Why?

5. What do honest people do that sets them apart?

6. When you correct a child for doing something wrong, how can your words, attitude, or tone make it easier for the child to come clean and tell you what happened? What are some words or attitudes that might discourage children from telling you the truth?

Child Scenario:
Daniel Comes Clean

Daniel's mom was in the kitchen making strawberry shortcake for a birthday party she was hosting for Daniel's grandfather. Daniel watched her cut up the strawberries, coat them with sugar, and set them in the refrigerator so the strawberries would be extra sweet and juicy.

Daniel asked his mom if he could have a strawberry.

"Not this time," she replied. "Your grandparents and all of your cousins are coming tonight, and we need to make sure we have enough for everyone."

After she finished, Daniel's mom wiped the countertops and said, "I have to return some books to the library and then swing by the grocery store. I'll be back in an hour."

Daniel watched his mom gather her purse and the library books, get in the car, and pull out of the driveway.

Alone, Daniel went to his room and played with a puzzle. After awhile he went back to the kitchen. Hmm, he thought to himself. Mom won't be back for an hour. I know she said not to eat any strawberries, but I only want a taste. I'll only take one so she won't notice, and there will still be plenty for Grandpa's birthday party.

Daniel went to the refrigerator and opened the door. He picked up the bowl of strawberries and lifted it to the countertop. However, the bowl was slick, and it slipped out of Daniel's hands. Before he could do anything about it, the bowl of strawberries crashed to the floor and juice went everywhere.

Daniel was horrified. He stared at the mess and wondered what he should do? Mom would be home soon, and she would be so upset with him.

Discussion Starters

1. How do you think Daniel's mom will react when she gets home?

2. If you were Daniel, what would you do about the strawberry mess?

3. What stories could Daniel concoct to explain what caused the mess and how the strawberries got ruined?

4. If Daniel confesses what he did, what do you think Daniel's mom will do? How will she react?

5. If Daniel cleans up the mess before his mom gets home and then doesn't tell her what happened, what do you think might happen? Will his mom ever find out? If so, how do you think she will react then?

6. How could Daniel have avoided this situation?

Teen Scenario:
Credit Where Credit Is Due

The local writer's guild was sponsoring a short story contest. It was open to anyone ages twelve to eighteen who lived in Regentsville. Charles had seen an advertisement at the library and decided to enter.

Charles had always enjoyed writing and people told him he was good at it. He thought it was fun to make up stories about fantastic characters in imaginary worlds. His imagination worked like a well-oiled machine, and with enough effort he could pump out a decent story in no time.

It was Thursday afternoon and the due date to turn in the short story was Saturday—plenty of time for someone as creative as Charles. As he sat in the library he decided to pull a couple of books from the fantasy section to give him some ideas. He found a book that featured twelve short stories about mythical creatures in another universe. The title of the third short story caught his eye, so he opened the book and began to read. Before he knew it he was immersed in the story. He could imagine himself as the author as it was just the type of thing he would write.

Then he got an idea. He could use this story from the book, change a few of the details to make it sound more like his own writing, and turn it in on Saturday. He was pretty sure the judges would be as crazy about the story as he was. No one would need to know that it wasn't his writing—it was pretty close to his writing anyway, right?

Discussion Starters

1. What is the problem with Charles's plan to use the story from the book?

2. If he changes a few details from the story, is it right to claim it as his own? Why or why not?

3. If Charles goes ahead with his plan and wins the contest, what could happen to him and his reputation if the judges discover the story is not his?

4. What would you do if you were Charles?

5. Why is it important to be honest with yourself and others?

6. Is it better to admit mistakes or to cover them up? Why is that?

Self-Control

· · · · · · · · · ·

doing what is right,
even when I don't
feel like it

Chapter 7
Self-Control

Imagine a young mother checking out at the grocery store with a two-year-old and an infant in her shopping cart. All of a sudden, the two-year-old begins throwing a fit. The mother tries to calm the child, but in the process, she loses her own temper and starts yelling at him. Next thing you know, the baby starts crying, too. Feeling embarrassed and frustrated, the mother leaves her groceries behind and shouts, "Enough!" as she rushes out of the store.

Or perhaps you're driving to work when you notice a small sports car weaving in and out of traffic. The driver of the sports car cuts off the driver of a pickup truck who slams on his brakes to avoid hitting the sports car. This upsets the driver in the pickup who starts honking his horn, flashing his lights, and tailgating the sports car. While focusing on the truck behind him, the sports car driver doesn't notice a van full of children slowing down in front of him, and the sports car rear ends the van.

Both of these sad stories have something in common—a person with a lack of self-control. When you lose control of your willpower and let emotions control you, bad things usually happen. Unfortunately, children who don't learn self-control often turn into teens or adults who lack self-control, which can lead to aggression, violence, addictions, and dysfunction at work and at home.

As we saw in the opening stories, losing your temper and flying into a rage can be costly. When you find yourself getting upset, take time to cool off before you say or do something you will regret.

It's natural to feel angry when something goes wrong or when your expectations are not met. Self-control means using anger as a signal that you need to dig deeper and figure out what's really happening. Maybe your expectations were unrealistic, or maybe what happened was an accident. Or perhaps an injustice needs to be corrected. Controlling your temper helps you think clearly and respond appropriately to the situation.

As the humorist Will Rogers once said, "Those who fly into a rage always make a bad landing." Stay in control of your temper and save yourself, and those you love, a lot of heartache.

In the 2015 Disney/Pixar animated movie *Inside Out*, a girl named Riley and her parents deal with a variety of emotions that influence how each person thinks and behaves. As the movie colorfully illustrates, part of growing up is learning how to process or control your emotions instead of letting them control you.

If you find yourself feeling upset, worried, discouraged, afraid, hurt, or annoyed—or maybe you just feel contrary and you can't put your finger on why yet—it's okay to say, "I'm not feeling well right now," or "I need some time to work through this."

68

What's not okay is using your feelings as an excuse to hurt yourself or someone else.

Take time to process what you're feeling. Write down your thoughts if that helps. Talk to someone you trust who can help you see things more clearly. Ask yourself, "Why do I feel this way?" or "Why does that bother me so much?"

Don't overlook the connection between physical health and emotional well-being. Simply put, it's hard to see situations clearly when we are tired, hungry, or in physical pain— not to mention what happens when we are chemically or hormonally unbalanced. If you struggle with chronic depression, please get help from a physician, nutritionist, or counselor.

As someone who regularly starts an exercise or diet program only to falter and fail after a certain period of time, the issue of willpower hits close to home for me. The problem begins when I think, "This extra serving won't hurt anything," or "I can skip my exercise routine this once."

The battle for self-control is usually won or lost in these little moments or small decisions. Unfortunately, once we cross over the line even a little bit, it is tempting to say, "What does it matter now," and then really let go of ourselves.

Self-control helps us stay on track and make the right decisions. By exercising willpower and self-discipline, we can avoid overspending, overeating, oversleeping, overworking, over-playing, or over-reacting. In the end, this makes life better for everyone.

Personal Reflection

1. What typically happens to you when you feel angry or upset? Does your heart beat faster or your mind get jumbled? Do you want to withdraw, do

you get louder, or do you go silent?

2. What should you do when you notice one of these physical signs?

3. Think of a time when you felt angry. What was the real problem? What was the solution?

4. Why is it important to control your temper? How does this protect you and others?

5. What are some healthy ways you can respond to frustration, disappointment, fear, loneliness, physical discomfort, or loss?

6. What should you do if you over-react and hurt someone with your words or actions?

7. What are some of your goals this year? How will your self-control be tested as you pursue these goals?

Child Scenario:
Becca Blows Up

Becca had been waiting for what seemed like forever to show the clay turtle she had made at the art center to her teacher, Ms. Griffith. But Ms. Griffith was still talking to Tommy and didn't seem to notice Becca standing there, waiting for her chance to speak.

Becca looked around at the classroom full of children. Some were working at math centers; others played with blocks or in the sandbox. She looked back at Ms. Griffith, still smiling and talking with Tommy. Finally, Tommy gave Ms. Griffith a hug and went back to his desk.

About time, thought Becca. She moved a little closer to Ms. Griffith when all of a sudden a voice came over the intercom: "Ms. Griffith, we need you to come to the office and meet Officer Lopez. We are sending a sub to watch your class for a few minutes while you are gone."

"Okay, I'll be right there," said Ms. Griffith as she turned and walked to the door to greet her substitute.

Becca's jaw dropped. She couldn't believe she had waited all this time and now Ms. Griffith was leaving just when it was Becca's turn to talk to her. Becca could feel her cheeks turning red. She spun around and was about to stomp back to her desk when she bumped into Lily who was standing behind her. Becca's little clay turtle flew out of her hand and hit the floor with a crash. Becca looked down to see her beautiful little turtle lying in pieces.

"Oh no!" said Lily. "I'm so sorry!"

"It's my fault," said Becca. "Don't worry about it."

Lily helped Becca clean up the mess, and then Becca went back to her desk, trying to hold back the tears.

Discussion Starters

1. What caused Becca to become frustrated?

2. How did Becca handle her frustration?

3. What could Becca have done differently to handle her frustration in a better way?

4. Is there a way Becca could have maybe gotten the

attention of Ms. Griffith without being rude or interrupting?

5. Was Becca right to feel frustrated? Why or why not?

6. Sometimes we can't help it when we start to feel an emotion like frustration, but it's what happens next that makes the difference. What is something Becca could have done when she first started to become frustrated?

7. Why did Becca say that breaking the turtle was her own fault and not Lily's?

8. How did Lily help her friend after the turtle broke?

9. How do you think Becca felt after the turtle broke?

10. Is it okay to cry when you are disappointed or sad? Why or why not?

11. What can you do after you cry to help yourself feel better?

Teen Scenario:
Disaster on the Diamond

The pressure was on. It had been a tough game between the Ponca City Wildcats and their rivals, the Enid Plainsmen. The score was tied three-to-three. Jackson was up to bat with a runner on second and third base. Jackson's team, the

Wildcats, had two outs this inning. If he could get on base, maybe the third base runner could reach home and move the team ahead.

The pitcher wound up and let go of the ball. It was a fastball, and it whizzed right past Jackson before he could even think. "Strike one!" yelled the umpire.

Jackson was a bit embarrassed and stepped out of the batter's box to collect himself. He stepped back in, turned to face the pitcher, and rolled the bat around in his hands. The pitcher drew back his arm and let the ball fly—this time almost nailing Jackson in the head. Jackson threw himself backward to avoid being hit, catching his cleats on the base and falling on his back.

That was all it took. The Wildcat bench emptied, and the players ran at the opposing team. Jackson picked himself up and charged at the pitcher. Despite the crowd of brawling players, Jackson landed a hard right punch straight on the pitcher's nose. The pitcher stumbled backward into the umpire who was trying to break up the fight.

The umpire yelled, "You're outta here!" and pointed at Jackson to leave the field.

Discussion Starters

1. How did Jackson feel when he missed the first pitch?

2. When the pitcher threw the second ball, do you think he almost hit Jackson on purpose? Does it matter whether it was on purpose or an accident?

3. Who caused Jackson to become angry and charge

the pitcher? Why do you think this?

4. Was Jackson responsible for his actions, or was it the pitcher's fault for almost hitting Jackson with the ball?

5. At what points could Jackson have taken control of his emotions and changed his course of action?

6. Do you think it was fair that Jackson was thrown out of the game? Why or why not?

7. How do you think Jackson felt when he was forced to leave the game?

8. Who gets hurt by Jackson's behavior on the baseball field?

Respect

· · · · · · · · ·

treating others with

honor and dignity

Chapter 8
Respect

Respect is a foundational character quality for having good relationships. When people do not value one another, it can lead to all kinds of negative outcomes such as hurt, irritation, abuse, manipulation, rejection, and violence. On the other hand, when people treat one another with honor and dignity it fosters positive results such as teamwork, harmony, cooperation, love, and kindness.

Respect is more than a feeling or attitude—it is acting in ways that value others. Consider the following attitudes and behaviors that demonstrate respect.

At its most basic level, we respect others because of their worth as human beings. We know to value everyone. Even if someone is a stranger, you can still treat the person with dignity. That's why we don't cut off people in traffic, step in front of someone waiting in line, or interrupt others when they are talking. At the very least, we should "do no harm" to the people we encounter.

We also practice common courtesy. Something as simple as good manners can go a long way toward showing respect for others. This includes holding the door instead of letting it slam in someone's face, practicing table manners, refraining from loud conversation at a library or theater, resisting the urge to interrupt, and other common courtesies.

In addition to the basic dignity everyone deserves as a human being, there is another level of honor or esteem we give based on someone's accomplishments or position. When life calls for it, we celebrate when someone wins a competition, earns a degree, or does something special, and we honor public servants, team leaders, older family members, and others who hold a special position in our lives or communities.

We learn to respect the differences in people, realizing that everyone has different talents, strengths, weaknesses, abilities, life experiences, family backgrounds, cultural norms, and personal beliefs. When we recognize and respect these differences, it helps us find common ground so we can live and work peacefully with one another.

Respecting differences does not mean you necessarily agree on everything or approve of what everyone does. You might say, "I guess we don't agree on that issue," or "We'll have to agree to disagree for now."

The key is to become a person who can disagree without being disagreeable.

The latter is easier if you practice self-respect. Not only should we value others and treat them with dignity, but we should also respect ourselves by protecting our minds and bodies from harm, developing our talents and strengths, and finding ways to do something positive. Doing so will prevent others from being able to drag you down by creating a false view of yourself.

Everyone is a special human being and offers something unique to the world—including you.

Personal Reflection

1. Is it possible to respect someone with whom you disagree? Why or why not?

2. How can teaching kids to respect others help them succeed in life?

3. What are some ways you can show children you value and respect them?

4. What are some ways your children can demonstrate respect for you?

5. Think about a current or historical event in which people did not respect each other. What happened as a result? What could have been done differently?

6. What is the danger in labeling people or groups without knowing them? Has anyone labeled you with a stereotype? How did that make you feel?

7. What does it mean to treat yourself with respect? How can you teach your children to respect themselves?

Child Scenario:
Srio's Birthday Surprise

You can't remember the last time you were so excited. There is new girl named Srio in the neighborhood, and you have been invited to a birthday party at her house this afternoon. Yesterday, you and your mom went shopping, and you took hours looking for the perfect present to buy. You found it at the last store: a beautiful stuffed kitty you know Srio will love. With the kitty between you on the front seat, your mom drives you to Srio's house and drops you off.

"I'll be back in an hour," Mom says with a wave.

You skip up the sidewalk and ring the doorbell. Inside, you hear a lot of loud voices speaking a language you don't recognize. After a moment, Srio opens the door.

"Hello," says Srio. Srio's mom also greets you; she is wearing a flowing colorful dress quite different from anything you've ever seen your mom wear, and you can't help but notice she has a bright red dot in the middle of her forehead. You try not to stare at Srio's mom as she welcomes you inside.

The first thing you notice is the house has a strong aroma coming from the kitchen. Srio's dad, his hair hanging in a long braid past his waist, stirs a big pot of spicy food. He smiles and invites you to join the family at the dinner table.

When you sit down, Srio's dad serves you a big plate of food that looks and smells like nothing you've had before. Everything is so different—you're not sure what to say or do.

Discussion Starters

1. What is so different about Srio's family? How do you feel being around people who are different from you?

2. How do you think Srio might feel visiting your home?

3. Is it polite to stare at the bright red dot on Srio's mom's forehead? Why or why not?

4. How can you show respect for different cultures and family backgrounds?

5. How can you learn about Srio's family culture in a respectful way?

Teen Scenario:
Rachel's Respect

You have known Rachel since you were six years old. Your parents and Rachel's parents were friends, and sometimes they would go out for the evening and hire a babysitter to watch you and Rachel. Your favorite game to play with Rachel back then was ponies; the two of you pretended to be ponies living over the rainbow.

Rachel has multiple sclerosis and has been in a wheelchair since eighth grade. Children that age can be cruel, and some of the neighborhood kids took to making fun of Rachel, calling her "Wheelie." They even made a game they called "Pop a Wheelie" where they would run past Rachel at school and thump her on the head. This always made you angry when you heard about it, but Rachel asked you to just let it go.

Now that you are in high school, you and Rachel don't see each other quite as often. She is in a community choir and you play basketball, so you run in different circles. On Thursday, just before practice, you hear your teammates talking. The new basketball coach is requiring team members to be more active in the community, participating in service projects or random acts of kindness.

One of your teammates, Chloe, suggests inviting Rachel to be the team mascot, noting this would not only make them look good to the coach, but it might also get Rachel's dad—

who owns a car dealership—to sponsor their new uniforms. "Who knows we might get to Pop a Wheelie and not have to worry about getting in trouble," she says with a laugh.

You had no idea that Chloe and the other girls were some of those who used to bully Rachel. Now it appears they want to use Rachel to make themselves look good and to get new uniforms. Even more disturbing is how this might cause the bullying and disrespect to start all over again for a girl who deserves so much better.

Discussion Starters

1. Do you tell the new coach about your teammates' plan? What could this accomplish?

2. Do you tell Rachel about what Chloe said? Do you tell Rachel's parents?

3. How does the disrespect being shown to your friend make you feel? How do your teammates feel?

4. What about this incident is most disturbing to you? How do you think it makes Rachel feel?

5. How should you treat people who are different from you?

6. What would school and society be like if people were more respectful to one another?

7. How can you show respect to siblings, parents, and other relatives?

Diligence

· · · · · · · · ·

focusing my effort

on the work at hand

Chapter 9
Diligence

No matter what subjects your children study, sports they play, instruments they learn, jobs they pursue, relationships they develop, or great accomplishments they hope to achieve, they must be able to focus their effort and attention on the task at hand in order to reach their full potential. Natural ability and good luck will only go so far—it takes diligence in order to excel.

There are many examples of diligence in this world. Consider Thomas Edison and his numerous inventions or NASA's effort to put a man on the moon. No doubt you have stories from your own life that illustrate the benefits of hard work.

One example that recently caught my attention was Tim Howard, goalkeeper for Team USA, who in 2014 broke a record for the number of saves in a World Cup soccer match. During an intense game against Belgium, Tim stayed calm under pressure and focused on his job, making an official fifteen saves. When asked later what it was like to be constantly under siege by his opponents, Tim replied, "That's my job. That's what I do."

This kind of focused effort led people to declare Tim Howard a "super keeper," but what makes his story more interesting is what Tim shares in his book, *The Keeper: A Life of Saving Goals and Achieving Them*, in which he describes his battle growing up with Tourette Syndrome and Obsessive Compulsive Disorder.

In short, focusing on his goals and not his disability allowed Tim to direct his energy toward becoming better on the soccer field. Ultimately, he turned his "disorders" into a competitive advantage.

Diligence can help people reach their full potential in any area. Whether the task is great or small, consider these points as you do your best:

1. Prepare.
Find out exactly what is expected for the job. Ask questions in order to clarify what you should do, when you should do it, and how it should be done. This will help you meet or exceed what is expected of you.

2. Focus.
Concentrate on the task at hand. Give your full attention and your full energy. Do not settle for half-hearted work or so-so results. Remove distractions (or remove yourself from distractions) so you can focus on your work.

3. Execute.
Do the job. Do not be a quitter. If the job seems too big, break it down into smaller steps. Build momentum by celebrating small "wins." Even if no one else knows all the effort you put into a task, you can still take personal satisfaction in a job well done.

Personal Reflection

1. What is the difference between doing a job half-heartedly and doing it diligently?

2. How can diligence make the difference between sloppy results and results you can be proud of?

3. What are some ways you can model diligence to your children?

4. What are some things you enjoy doing? Why is it easier to be diligent when you enjoy what you do? How can you be diligent even if you don't enjoy a particular job or task?

5. How can breaking a difficult task into smaller steps help you accomplish your goal?

6. Why is it important to celebrate with your children when they do a job right? How can you celebrate when they work hard and finish a task?

Child Scenario:
Katie's Big Job

It was Peach Festival time in Katie Tucker's hometown, and it seemed like everyone was involved in some way to make the Peach Festival a big success. The Carson family was in charge of advertising the festival in the paper. The Bensons, Smiths, and Greens set up all the tables and tents. Other families baked cookies and cakes, and local musicians provide just the right kind of festive background music.

Every year, Katie's family made peach ice cream. In fact, their peach ice cream was so popular they would usually run out by early afternoon. Everyone in her family had a job to do when making and selling the ice cream. Katie's mom mixed the ingredients and put them in the ice cream machine. Her dad drove the truck and loaded and unloaded all the supplies. Katie's big brother, Ben, was in charge of filling the ice cream machine with ice and keeping it running smoothly. Katie's older sister, Dani, scooped the ice cream out of the machine and put it in plastic cups to sell to the people in line. And Katie's job was to put a sticker on every cup that said "Tucker's Delicious Peach Ice Cream."

Katie's job wasn't easy. Every year, things got very busy at the Tucker family's ice cream stand. There were always a lot of people in line, and every member of her family rushed here and there trying to get everything done.

Katie had to concentrate on her job. First she had to count out the sheets of stickers and the rows of empty cups in order to make sure she had enough stickers. Then she had to put the stickers on the cups one by one, making sure she didn't miss a single one. After the stickers were on the cups, she handed them to her sister Dani who would fill the cups with ice cream for the customers.

If Katie wasn't careful and didn't pay attention, she could drop the cups or forget to put the stickers on before handing them to Dani. Or worse, she could knock the empty cups to the ground, and then she would have to start all over.

Discussion Starters

1. Why is it important for Katie to do her job for this family activity well?

2. How does Katie's family depend on her?

3. What does it mean to be diligent?

4. How does Katie demonstrate that she is diligent when doing her job?

5. What might happen if Katie forgets to put the stickers on the cups, or if she drops the cups?

6. How does being diligent help Katie not make mistakes?

7. How do you think Katie feels when she does a good job?

Teen Scenario:
Desi's Big Project

The history of the American Civil War might not be Desi's favorite subject in school but she was old enough to know that didn't mean she could skip it. She had a big, thick textbook from her teacher that she was supposed to read, notes she was supposed to take, and most important of all, a big battlefield project she had to design and complete on deadline.

First, Desi had to read all about a Civil War battle of her choosing. Then she had to write step-by-step the sequence of events that happened before, during, and after the battle. But the biggest part of the project was making a model of the battle with poster board and clay, complete with fake trees, bushes, grass, and watercolor paint.

Even though she didn't like reading about wars, Desi knew it was important to give the project her best effort. Everyone's Civil War project would be entered into a competition, and the top three projects would win a prize.

Desi chose to study "Pickett's Charge" during the Battle of Gettysburg, Pennsylvania. She looked up information in her textbook and did extensive online research. She read, studied, and took notes. Then she made a detailed list of everything that led up to the battle, what happened during Pickett's Charge, and the outcome.

Desi collected all the supplies she needed to build her battlefield model. She had two large poster boards, markers, paints, small bushes, and even some little plastic army guys that her brother supplied, which she painted blue and gray for the different armies. Using what she learned from her research, she carefully constructed an accurate depiction of the event as it occurred on July 3, 1863.

On the day of the competition, Desi took her model up to the classroom where all the projects were on display. She filled out an information sheet with her name, entry number, and the title of the project. She placed the information sheet under the model just as she was instructed to do. Then she went back into the hall to wait with the other contestants.

After about an hour, the judges called all the contestants into the room and announced the results. Desi had won second place! She beamed with excitement when her name was called and happily received her red ribbon from the judges.

Discussion Starters

1. Why was it important for Desi to do her best on the school project?

2. How did Desi's diligence pay off in the end?

3. What are some things Desi did that showed her diligence?

4. What do you think would have happened if Desi put less effort into building her model?

5. How do you think Desi felt when she won second place?

6. Even if Desi hadn't received an award, what did she learn or gain through the process of doing her project?

7. How do you think Desi will do in school and in life if she keeps up this kind of diligence, focus, and commitment to do her best?

8. What are some common tasks, projects, chores, or assignments you do? How can you be diligent when working on them?

Obedience

• • • • • • • • •

doing my duty with a
good attitude

Chapter 10
Obedience

The word "obedience" generates mixed reaction in people. Some recognize that without law and order, the world would be a more dangerous place. Others hesitate to use the word because it seems too authoritarian or controlling, also a valid concern. Differences such as these underscore why it is so important to talk about obedience with your children, if only so you have a mutual understanding of what it is—and what it is not.

As a parent or caregiver, you are responsible for the proper upbringing of your children. This includes guiding and instructing them until they take their places in the adult world. Early in life, many instructions given to children are for their own health and safety: "Don't touch the stove." "Stay out of the street." "Come quickly when I call for you."

As children mature, you can shed light on the reasons behind your instructions so they know why they should or shouldn't do things. This will help them think for themselves instead of blindly following orders. It will also help you clarify your purpose and intent behind the instructions.

Unfortunately, not everyone in the world has a child's best interest at heart. That is why we must help children understand the difference between a teacher who says, "Get in the room quickly and close the door," and a stranger who says, "Get in the car quickly and close the door."

One trick used by child predators is instructing victims not to tell anyone else about what happened but to "keep it a secret just between them." Warn your children about the dangers of keeping secrets and encourage them to tell you right away about anything they don't think is right.

Just because something is lawful or reasonable doesn't make it easy, pleasant, or fun. This is where obedience usually becomes an issue. It is easy to do things we like, but more difficult to do things we don't like to do.

In practical terms, obedience is fulfilling our duties with a good attitude. This means responding quickly instead of delaying, completing a job instead of leaving parts unfinished, and having a cooperative spirit instead of grumbling or complaining. Some jobs or assignments are not much fun, but feeling sorry for yourself won't make the task easier. In contrast, working with a positive attitude usually makes the job go faster and better for everyone.

A cooperative person honors the spirit of the law instead of just focusing on the letter of the law. If a teacher says, "Please pay attention," a reasonable student would interpret that to mean "be quiet and focus on your work." An uncooperative student, however, might play on his cell phone and claim he was following the teacher's instruction. After all, the teacher had only said to "pay attention." And the student was paying attention to his phone, right?

I am convinced you can never make enough rules to stop someone who is manipulative or rebellious. Faced with a new rule, such people just become more creative rule-breakers. The only lasting solution is to help them develop the inward character and motivation to fulfill their duties, honor others, control their actions, and do the right thing.

Children who develop a proper understanding of obedience, cooperation, and duty have a better chance of becoming adults who appreciate law, order, and personal responsibility. That, in turn, makes life better for everyone in society—including the next generation.

Personal Reflection

1. What are some duties you are expected to fulfill as a parent? As an employee? As a citizen?

2. As you fulfill your duties, how can your attitude affect the quality of your work?

3. How do you feel when you have to tell your children again and again to do something?

4. How does it make life easier when everyone in your family fulfills their duties with a good attitude?

5. What are some situations in which you don't want your children to do as they are told? How can you teach this to your children?

6. Some families establish an emergency code word in case the parents need to send a stranger to pickup their children, so the children know it is okay. Do you have a plan for dealing with situations like this?

7. How can you teach your children to say "no" when something doesn't seem right? What are some words they can say? What are some actions they can take?

8. How would you like your children to approach you if they are unsure about an instruction or have information that might change your mind? Are you open to hearing their appeal?

Child Scenario:
Elijah Says Yes!

It was the end of November and time to decorate for Christmas. Elijah was excited because today they were going to set up the Christmas tree. His dad had gone into the attic and brought down the big box that contained the artificial tree they set up each year, and Mom had baked cookies for everyone to snack on as they set up the tree and put on the decorations.

Everyone was smiling and having a good time except for Susan, Elijah's older sister. Susan was sitting in the corner, staring at her phone, listening to her music with earbuds. She's probably texting her boyfriend, thought Elijah as he glanced in Susan's direction.

Susan noticed him looking at her and scowled at him. For just a moment, Elijah was sad and a little frustrated with his sister for being such a grouch, but then his mom came into the room with a plateful of fresh cookies and Elijah forgot all about his sullen sister.

Elijah's dad had taken the lights out of the box and begun testing each string; Elijah helped him replace a few burnt-out bulbs. Dad and Mom set up the tree and put the lights on the branches. Then it was Elijah and Susan's turn to help. Elijah stood to help his mom hang the garland. Then his dad looked over at Susan, "Hey Susie Q," he cheerfully said. (Susie Q was Susan's nickname ever since she was a baby.) "Time to join the family and help us make this tree look gorgeous!" Susan glared at her parents, got up from her seat, and began hanging old-fashioned glass balls on the branches.

Discussion Starters

1. Who do you think had a better time decorating the tree, Elijah or Susan? Why?

2. Did Susan still have to help even though she was grouchy? Do you think this made her feel happier or grouchier?

3. What was Elijah's attitude during the decorating?

4. How do you think Elijah's attitude made his parents feel? How do you think Susan's attitude made her parents feel?

5. How did Susan's bad attitude affect Elijah? Did he let it bother him for long?

6. Elijah demonstrated a lot of maturity by not letting Susan's attitude ruin his day. What did he do after he initially felt upset?

7. How could Susan have made the day go better for everyone?

Teen Scenario:
The Letter of the Law

Stacey and Nicole had asked for permission to have a party for the jazz band in the school gymnasium. The principal hesitantly agreed. He was a bit reluctant to allow another party because the last time a group had used the gym the floor had been damaged, costing the school a lot of money in repairs.

After a lot of begging and reminding the principal of all the jazz band contributed to the school community, the principal finally consented, but he gave the girls a sheet with rules they needed to follow in order to have the party.

The list included: No red drinks, no sticky food, make sure everyone stays in the gym and doesn't wander around the school, and clean up after yourselves.

The girls gladly took the list and promised the principal that they would do as he asked.

Later that afternoon, Stacey and Nicole went to the store with their list to buy supplies for the party.

"No red drinks," Nicole said as they strolled the soda aisle.

They looked around and bought several varieties of soda, and then they saw a drink that looked perfect for their party. It was called Red Rocket and had a picture of a strawberry on the label. Stacey picked up a bottle and put it in the cart.

"Wait a minute," said Nicole "we aren't supposed to serve red drinks."

"I think it's more of dark pink color," she said with a grin.

She and Nicole giggled. In the next aisle they picked up some chips, nuts, chocolate, cookies, and jelly beans.

"Don't even say it!" snapped Stacey as Nicole shook her head at the big bag of jelly beans in her friend's hand. "Jelly beans aren't so sticky. They have a hard crunchy outside and only get sticky when they're in your mouth about to be swallowed."

The girls giggled again, and took their purchases to the cashier and checked out.

Discussion Starters

1. What do you think it means to follow the letter of the law but ignore the spirit or intent of the law?

2. How did Stacey and Nicole technically obey what the principal had asked them to do?

3. Do you think the principal will be happy with their decision?

4. How likely do you think the principal will be to let them use the gym the next time they ask?

5. How does their decision affect the possibility that others will get to use the gym in the future?

6. How easy could it have been for Stacey and Nicole to follow the letter and the spirit of the law? What could they have done differently?

Orderliness

· · · · · · · · ·

keeping things clean

and neat

Chapter 11
Orderliness

Families today tend to be very busy. The days are packed with work and school, and evenings are filled with sports, music, family, or community activities—not to mention household chores and homework. As parents, we spend a lot of time driving children here and there, hoping they have everything they need so we don't have to swing by the house for a third time to pick something up someone forgot.

All of this rushing about can create a feeling of chaos in our lives, leaving us with little time to organize our thoughts or surroundings. Wouldn't it be nice to feel ahead of the game, to be less rushed, and able to enjoy a more peaceful and orderly life? Part of teaching children how to be successful is to equip them with the skills they need to be orderly. Orderliness is more than keeping a clean bedroom with furniture neatly arranged, clothes put away, and a freshly made bed. Orderliness includes how you use your time, how you solve problems, and how you plan and execute tasks.

Here are a few simple ways you and your children can make orderliness a habit:

Simplify your stuff. The fewer things that clutter your life, the less effort you have to put in to keep things neat. At our home we do not have an attic for storing things. This is on purpose, because we found over the years that an attic only encouraged us to store things for which we had no use.

When we decided to convert our attic into living space, we went through everything we had collected. Each thing that had not been used in six months was given away or discarded. We asked ourselves, "If we died tomorrow, would we want to make our children deal with all this stuff? This item in my hand . . . would our children want it?" If the answer was no, we decided to give it away or discard it. When finished, everything we wanted to keep fit into one closet, including Christmas decorations.

A similar process can work for you and your children. Routinely go through drawers, cabinets, closets, storage spaces, and under the beds. Give away or discard things you or your children no longer need, wear, or play with. With fewer things taking up space, you will have more room to work and play—and you will spend less time putting stuff away.

Put away what you're finished with before getting out more. A tidy room or house can quickly become a mess when things keep coming out and nothing is put away—whether toys, clothes, books, food, or household projects. Discuss this with your children and strike an agreement to help one another follow this principle. This means giving your children permission to respectfully say something when they see you forget to put things away. And of course, you get to remind them, too.

Tidy your space. From time to time, send children with a plastic bag to clean out trash in the car, around your house, and in their rooms. Work together to clean house or divide up jobs such as dusting, sweeping, or vacuuming. Teach children how to clean their own bathrooms and take responsibility for their own space. Whether they realize it or not, keeping things clean and neat will make your home brighter, fresher, and less stressful.

Know your schedule. For young children, you might put a sheet of paper on the refrigerator that shows all seven days of the week, or use a monthly calendar if you prefer. Work with your children each week to write down the major activities you plan to do (or draw pictures if your children do not read yet). Let your children cross out each day so they can see where in the month they are. Don't forget to add clean up times into your weekly schedule or one day each month to de-clutter.

For older children, work together to create a more detailed schedule that includes departure times, lists of anything they need to bring or prepare, and maybe even the weather forecast so they can plan what to wear. This sounds like work, but a weekly planning session lets you communicate with your children and learn what is going on in their lives. They can also get a glimpse of what is happening in your life, and it teaches them good planning skills.

Don't let chaos rule your life. Develop orderly habits that foster peace and stability for yourself and the ones you love.

Personal Reflection

1. What are some of the advantages of having a neat and orderly home?

2. How can being neat and orderly help you be more efficient with your time?

3. What are some ways you can encourage your children when you see them practicing orderliness?

4. What are some guidelines or expectations you have regarding neatness?

5. Are you a detailed planner, or do you roll from one thing to the next without much planning? What about others in your household?

6. How can a weekly planning session improve communication with family members?

7. What are two things you can do differently in order to become more orderly?

Child Scenario:
Late to the Party!

Tanya had just finished watching her favorite show on television. Now she was going to her bedroom to play with her miniature action figures. She shoved open her door, which wasn't easy because of all the stuff she had left on the floor from the day before—well, maybe many days before.

Tanya carefully walked around the piles of toys and clothes until she found the toy box. She opened the lid and looked, but there wasn't anything inside except a doll and a couple of blocks. She sighed and glanced around the room; she couldn't see any of her action figures because everything was so messy.

Tanya's mom hollered from down the hall, "Isn't today Becca's birthday party?"

Tanya stopped in her tracks. Yes, it was, but she couldn't remember the time. She frantically looked around. Where is that invitation, Tanya wondered.

She dug through the piles of things on the floor. The more she dug, the more panicked she became. Where was the invitation. Is it over there. No. What about under this stuff? Nope. Under the bed maybe? No again. Ugh! I'll never find it. After twenty minutes of searching, Tanya saw something bright pink sticking out from behind the clothes hamper.

"I found it!" she yelled.

Tanya quickly opened the invitation and was in disbelief. The party had started two hours ago.

Tanya quickly dressed, wrapped the birthday present she had bought earlier in the week, and got in the car. After being dropped off at Becca's house, Tanya knocked on the front door. Becca's brother answered and showed Tanya to the backyard where everyone was cleaning up after cake, ice cream, and a rousing game of tetherball.

"I'm so sorry!" Tanya said, handed her the present.

"It's okay," sighed Becca. "We are almost finished cleaning up, and then it will be time for everyone to go home."

Tanya helped clean up after the party and said good-bye to Becca. Back home, Tanya took another look at her messy room. She began to clean, straighten, and organize. I don't want to miss another party, she told herself.

Discussion Starters

1. Why was the party invitation difficult to find?

2. How did having a messy room make it difficult for Tanya to move around?

3. If the room had been neat, would it have been easier for Tanya to see the invitation?

4. What are some things Tanya could start doing that would make her room more neat and orderly?

5. How can you keep track of important events so you don't forget about them?

Teen Scenario:
Late to Practice!

"Three minutes! You have three minutes, and I need you dressed and on the field ready to play!" your coach shouts.

Frantically you look around, digging like a dog after a lost bone through the mound of stuff in the bottom of your locker. Where are my cleats, you wonder as your heart beats quickly. Your eyes dart from item to item—water bottle, spare socks, jersey—whew, there are my cleats! You grab your cleats and try to put them on as you run to the field—hopping on the right foot, then the left. Your team is doing push-ups in unison as your coach watches you staggering out late, trying to tie your shoes and walk all at the same time.

Discussion Starters

1. How does being neat and orderly help you find things when you need them?

2. How can being organized help others know they can depend on you? Why would a coach value that in a player? Why would a boss?

3. How does it make you feel when you're running late and you can't find what you need? In comparison, how do you feel when you know you have everything in hand and under control?

4. Can being disorganized affect how you complete your school assignments? How?

5. Why is it important to plan ahead?

6. How can planning ahead and organizing your mind help you be prepared for things even when they are unexpected?

7. How does an organized space help you be less stressed? How does it save you time?

8. What are some things you can do to become more organized and orderly?

Enthusiasm

· · · · · · · · · ·

putting my whole

heart into what I

do

Chapter 12
Enthusiasm

Enthusiasm is a contagious attitude that can inspire and uplift those around you. Whether you sport a pleasant smile or give an encouraging word, your spark of energy and excitement can brighten your day and ignite others to live with enthusiasm.

In a group setting, enthusiasm is often called "team spirit," and it can make a big difference in how the group performs. Teams that are excited about the game and participate with enthusiasm have a great advantage over teams that lose heart or don't care.

People who put their whole heart into what they do also increase their chance of happiness and success. This applies to students at school, employees on the job, parents raising their children, or families being involved in their communities. People who live with passion naturally find more fulfillment than those who muddle their way through each day.

Something that fuels enthusiasm is vision. When you know what you need to do and why it is important, it becomes easier to invest yourself in that project. For example, when you have a long-term view of raising your children, it helps you endure the difficult moments and continue investing in their future. When you see the value in each day, it motivates you to spend your time wisely. When you see how your job impacts others, it inspires you to do your very best.

Another key to enthusiasm is relationships. It is energizing to be with people who are positive, optimistic, hopeful, cheerful, and energetic. Spend time with people who encourage and strengthen you, and be that kind of person for others—especially for your children as you model this important attitude.

Enthusiasm does not mean you ignore reality and pretend everything is fine when it is not. An enthusiastic person sees problems for what they are and decides to work through them with a positive attitude instead of giving up or losing heart.

Enthusiasm is something we choose, not just feel. Sometimes we don't feel very enthusiastic, but we can still choose to do our best, encourage others, and not give up. Pretty soon, our emotions might catch up with our actions, and we can start feeling enthusiastic again.

Personal Reflection

1. When is it easy to be enthusiastic about something? When is it difficult to be enthusiastic?

2. How does enthusiasm make life better for you and others?

3. What do you think is the difference between enthusiasm and hype?

4. How does "team spirit" impact you and the people you live with or work with?

5. What are some differences between someone who is an energy-giver versus an energy-drainer?

6. How can you have a positive attitude when doing something you don't feel like doing?

7. Why is it important to always do your best, even if others aren't watching?

8. Think of people you know who are enthusiastic. How do you feel when you are around them?

Child Scenario:
Turning Around

Joanna was feeling a little down. She had gone to the park earlier in the day and had accidentally left her favorite stuffed dog on the slide. When she realized what had happened and went back to get it, the stuffed dog was gone.

Joanna's mom came into her room to let her know it was about time to leave for her soccer game. Even though she didn't feel like it, Joanna knew she should go to the game— her team needed her.

When she arrived at the soccer field and got out of the car, Joanna was enthusiastically greeted by her best friend, Hannah.

Hannah had seen Joanna's car pull into the parking lot and was already halfway to the car when Joanna opened the door. "Hey Jo!" yelled Hannah as she ran up to Joanna and gave her a big hug. Joanna was already starting to feel a little better.

Hannah immediately began telling Joanna about a new kitten her uncle had given her and her sister. "Oh Jo!" she exclaimed, "You just have to come and see him. He is the cutest little ball of fur I've ever seen!" As Joanna began to think about holding Hannah's kitten, she actually began to smile.

Joanna and Hannah walked together to where their team was getting ready for the game. Hannah whispered to Joanna, "You're going to do great today, Jo! You are such a fast runner; I just know we have a good chance to win."

By now, Joanna was feeling pretty great. Just being around Hannah made her smile, and Hannah's sincere enthusiasm was just the thing Joanna needed to turn her day around.

Discussion Starters

1. What happened early in the day that made Joanna feel sad?

2. When Joanna arrived at the game, what was the first thing that happened that began to make her feel better?

3. What did Hannah do to show her enthusiasm?

4. How did Joanna's mood change as she was with her friend Hannah?

5. How is enthusiasm contagious?

6. How can your attitude impact those around you?

Teen Scenario:
Choose Your Captain

It was the day before Piper's gymnastics team elected a new team captain. Being team captain was a big deal—the captain was responsible for contacting everyone to make sure they knew the time and location of every competition, making sure all appropriate forms were completed, and organizing special events such as movie nights and social gatherings. Two girls had put their names in the running for captain: Piper and Elisa.

Piper was an enthusiastic young lady. She always had a smile and a word of encouragement for the girls on the team. She would often arrive early to help set up for practice and stay late to clean up the equipment and make sure each girl had a ride home. She also regularly invited the team to her house for games and snacks in an effort to build team spirit. Piper made signs for the competitions and could always be seen on the sidelines, encouraging her teammates.

Elisa, on the other hand, was more distant and aloof. She didn't enjoy gymnastics all that much—it was something her mother expected her to do so she reluctantly agreed. A bit moody and difficult to predict, Elisa often criticized her teammates during practice. Just a few minutes around Elisa could make even the happiest person start to feel a bit down. She usually arrived late to practice and couldn't wait to leave when it was over. She mainly put her name in for captain because she thought it would make her mother happy.

Discussion Starters

1. Who do you think will be elected captain of the gymnastics team? Why do you think this?

2. What kind of person would you rather spend time with: Piper or Elisa? Why?

3. What are some ways Piper demonstrates enthusiasm?

4. What effect do you think Piper's enthusiasm has on her teammates?

5. What message does it send when Elisa is one of the last to arrive and the first to leave?

6. How might Elisa's attitude change if she was doing something she cared about?

7. Sometimes you don't get to choose what you do at school or at work. How can you still be enthusiastic in these situations?

Determination

• • • • • • • • •

overcoming obstacles in

order to reach my goal

Chapter 13
Determination

There is something about an underdog team or comeback story that appeals to human nature. Perhaps it is the pursuit of winning, the struggle to overcome odds, or the idea that even "little people" have the potential to do great things. Determination involves all of these aspects, which makes it an inspiring character quality to observe in others and practice ourselves.

Life is not always easy, and anything worth achieving usually involves a lot of hard work. Even the most talented athletes, the smartest scientists, and the most successful business leaders will tell you it takes more than raw talent, intelligence, or good luck to succeed. You must practice, study, prepare, and push yourself to continually do better. And that takes determination.

Determination is something your children will need throughout their lives. Like a toddler learning to walk, they must be able to pick themselves up off the ground and try again. This kind of perseverance, resilience, and grit is essential for succeeding in school, keeping a good job, reaching financial goals, building healthy habits, developing strong relationships, raising the next generation of children, and pursuing personal dreams and ambitions. A child with determination does not lose heart, does not give up, and does not settle for anything less than his or her best.

In an article titled "Creating Determined Kids" in the January 2015 issue of *Character Core Magazine*, Dr. Grace Wilson, a licensed marriage and family therapist, shares the following advice:

"Perhaps you've seen a child struggle with a task that is just above his or her current ability. As a parent or caregiver, it can be difficult to watch the struggle, and you might be tempted to step in and make sure the child doesn't fail. However, this kind of 'rescue' is less likely to teach children determination and more likely to teach them they are unable to accomplish difficult tasks on their own."

Dr. Wilson suggests five ways to help children develop determination, which we will explore:

1. Praise their efforts.
Instead of focusing solely on outcomes, results, or achievements, recognize when children give their best effort and compliment their character. Praising children for having the right attitude and effort focuses on something within their control instead of basing your praise on outcomes that are often beyond their control.

2. Encourage them.
When you see children facing an obstacle or struggling through a situation, encourage them to stick with tasks a little longer and not give up. Remind them of the goal and why it matters. Perhaps your

words of encouragement will help them push through and finish the job.

3. Provide help when asked without taking over.
If your child asks for help, be careful you don't end up taking over the job and doing it yourself. This robs your children from learning how to work through obstacles and find creative solutions. It also robs them of the satisfaction that comes from accomplishing a difficult task. Instruct, coach, and encourage—but let your children do the work.

4. Teach them how to manage failure.
Whether your children miss an answer at school, lose a ball game, or blow a special opportunity, failure is an inevitable part of life they must learn how to manage. There is a big difference between recognizing that you failed and feeling like a failure. Children who see failure as part of the learning process will rebound faster and better than those who treat failure as part of their personal identity.

5. Demonstrate determination.
As with any other character quality, your children are watching how you practice this principle yourself. The way you respond to life's challenges will speak much louder than anything you tell your children about determination.

Helping children build determination is one of the best things you can do for them in the long run. Once learned, for the rest of their lives it will empower them to work through challenges, maintain strong relationships, and make the most of their lives in good times and bad.

Personal Reflection

1. Think of people who inspire you by their determination. What is it they do that is inspirational? What type of attitude do they exhibit?

2. Why is it important to praise attitude and effort, not just the results or outcome?

3. When your child asks for help, do you tend to take over the task? How can you help without taking over?

4. How do you handle failure? How do your children handle failure? Is there room for improvement in this area?

5. When in your life have you pushed through with determination in order to reach a goal? How did it feel when you finally succeeded? What would have happened if you gave up and quit?

Child Scenario:
A Card for Grandmother

Graciela held the crayon steady in her little hand as she carefully wrote "H a p p y" at the top of the construction paper. She smiled and, with a look of deep concentration, began writing the next word: "B i . . ." Suddenly her hand slipped, and she dropped the crayon. The crayon slowly rolled to the edge of the table and fell to the floor. "Oh no!" she exclaimed, "I'll never be able to do this right, and I want it to be special for Grandma."

Graciela's mother came over to see what was going on.

"I am proud of how hard you are working," she said, as she gave Graciela a hug. "Grandma will love the card because you made it for her." Graciela looked up and smiled at her mom. It seemed like her mom always knew exactly what to say to make her want to try again. Graciela picked her crayon back up and continued writing: ". . . r t h d a y."

"There I did it!" said Graciela, beaming with happiness.

"I knew you could," said mother as she gave Graciela a wink and a smile.

Discussion Starters

1. How did Graciela feel when she dropped the crayon?

2. What did Graciela's mother do that encouraged her not to give up?

3. How did Graciela feel after her mother's talk?

4. Why do you think Graciela decided to try again?

5. How did Graciela feel when she was successful?

6. The next time Graciela faces a challenge, do you think she will give up or try harder?

Teen Scenario:
The Big Race

You have decided to run a half-marathon (13.1 miles) in a few months to help raise support for a local charity. Think about the following things:

Discussion Starters

1. What are some ways you will prepare for the half-marathon?

2. What can you do when you get tired of practicing and preparing for the marathon?

3. What will happen if you give up and decide not to keep working prior to the marathon?

4. What are some of the challenges you predict you will face while preparing and while running the marathon?

5. What will you do to overcome those challenges?

6. Would it help to have a friend prepare and participate with you? Why or why not?

7. How can having someone to encourage you help build your determination?

8. Think about right after the marathon is finished. How do you think you will feel once you cross the finish line? How does imagining your success help you maintain your determination?

Conclusion

A childhood friend and I were recently talking about the small Oklahoma town where we grew up just one block away from each other. My friend had a paper route and knew everyone in town. In contrast, I was new to the neighborhood and didn't know anyone. I was ten years old at the time—a rather awkward and difficult age for me. I enjoyed horses and playing piano, but baseball was also high on my list. That's where Mr. Robinson enters the story.

Mr. Robinson lived next door and had two children about my age. On many summer evenings, Mr. Robinson would gather the neighborhood children for a game of baseball in his backyard. His children were quite good, but they still invited me to play even though I was a rank amateur.

Mr. Robinson was a truly caring person—not only to children, but to others in the community. No matter what we wanted to talk about, Mr. Robinson gave us the feeling that what we had to say mattered to him. And I think it did.

One evening we were playing baseball in his backyard and it was getting late. "One more inning!" shouted Mr.

Robinson, who served as pitcher so everyone had a chance to hit the ball. Mr. Robinson wound up, leaned forward, and pitched the ball—which promptly sailed right past the batter and through Mr. Robinson's own window!

I remember the silence like it was yesterday. We all looked at each other and wondered what Mr. Robinson would do. We waited and watched . . . and then we saw Mr. Robinson crack a smile. His smile turned into a chuckle, which then turned into a big belly laugh. Soon Mr. Robinson had all of us laughing at the irony of the situation.

Mr. Robinson taught me a valuable lesson that day. He showed me that people are more precious than possessions, that good relationships are more important than glass windows, and that sometimes the best thing we can do is laugh at our mistakes and move on with life.

Those are lessons I want to teach my children and grandchildren as they learn and grow. I want them to know they are marvelous individuals with incredible potential. I want them to know they are deeply loved and worth more than any window pane. I want them to have the type of character that treats others with kindness and concern no matter what they can or can't do for them in return. And when life throws them a curve ball, I hope they know how to laugh and make the most of it.

Together we can help the next generation lead positive and productive lives filled with good character qualities. Hopefully in fifty years they can tell their friends about the valuable lessons they learn from us today.

What could be a more worthy goal and legacy, than leaving behind a generation of positive people.

About the Author

Dr. Virginia Jennison Smith's other works include *Engage: An Active Response to Bullying*, a research-based approach to identify, prevent, and respond to bullying and aggression in schools; *Elevate: Take Your Game to the Highest Level*, a program designed to help coaches and parents teach and model character in athletics; *Goal*, a sports and character program for younger children; and *Third Culture Kids: Retention and Persistence When Repatriating to Attend University*.

Dr. Smith also presents on such topics as Classroom Management, Positive Discipline, Conflict Resolution, Teaming with Parents, Bully Prevention, and Creating a Culture of Character in Your Classroom.

For Strata Leadership, she has also developed the Cultural Analysis, a research instrument to assess the culture of organizations and help them implement improvements. As the editor of the *Character Core Magazine*, she writes a monthly article about character in organizations.

She lives in Edmond, Oklahoma, with her husband, Patrick, a university professor.